HISTORY & GEOGRAPHY 1007
The Industrial Revolution

LIFEPAC Test is located in the center of the booklet. Please remove before starting the unit.

Author:
William A. Alexander

Editor-in-Chief:
Richard W. Wheeler, M.A.Ed.

Editors:
Douglas Williamson
Jean Turner

Consulting Editor:
Howard Stitt, Th.M Ed.D.

Revision Editor:
Alan Christopherson, M.S.

MEDIA CREDITS:
Page 6: © Matejh photography, iStock, Thinkstock; **11**: © Photos.com, Thinkstock; **15**: © Patriek Vandenbussche, iStock, Thinkstock; **24**: © Yvonne Haugen, iStock, Thinkstock; **32**: © Baloncici, iStock, Thinkstock; © Jupiterimages, Photos.com, Thinkstock; **43**: © bijendra, iStock, Thinkstock; **47**: © jgshields, iStock, Thinkstock; **53**: © McInich, iStock, Thinkstock.

Alpha Omega
PUBLICATIONS

804 N. 2nd Ave. E.
Rock Rapids, IA 51246-1759

THE INDUSTRIAL REVOLUTION

Introduction

Prior to the mid 1700s, the lifestyle of the United States was basically simple. Although labor was difficult and often seemed endless, it was ultimately satisfying. Man's position of preeminence as the earthly provider and creator of life's necessities gave him a feeling of worth and importance. Food, clothing, tools, and furnishings were all supplied by the toil of man's hand. With the advent of the machine age, man's existence drastically changed. The wonders of industry quickly spread throughout the world, replacing the muscle of man with the power of the machine. Industry expanded to all aspects of life.

In this LIFEPAC® you will examine the Industrial Revolution and its changing effects upon man and upon his world. From Europe's Middle Ages you will discover the steps leading to industry's birth, and you will follow the Industrial Revolution as it set the wheels of industry in motion in England and elsewhere in Europe. You will also watch the age of industry change America into a powerful industrialized nation. You will also study the drastic change the Industrial Revolution brought to the lifestyle of the working man. In addition, you will experience the hardships and the injustices working men faced, and their struggle to share in the wealth they were producing. Finally, you will study the accomplishments of the age of industry, examining the Industrial Revolution's influence on production, distribution, and the world economy.

Man lives in an incredible age, surrounded by powerful machines and by labor-saving devices. Hopefully, after studying this LIFEPAC, you will view the Industrial Revolution as something more than just another meaningless vocabulary term. The Industrial Revolution is a vital, living reality that became the determining factor behind the prosperous economy you know and enjoy today.

Objectives

Read these objectives. The objectives tell you what you will be able to do when you have successfully completed this LIFEPAC. When you have finished this LIFEPAC, you should be able to:

1. List the early European influences that affected the beginning of the Industrial Revolution.

2. Describe the early industrial developments and inventions that advanced industry's growth in Europe and England.

3. List the factors that made the early United States ripe for industry.

4. Explain the influence of wars on industry and the effects of industry on war.

5. Describe the advantages and disadvantages of the growth and influence of corporations on the economy.

6. List the technological developments that greatly increased United States productivity.

7. Explain the social changes that resulted from the Industrial Revolution.

8. Describe the influence of the Industrial Revolution on the world's economy.

Survey the LIFEPAC. Ask yourself some questions about this study and write your questions here.

1. INDUSTRIAL REVOLUTION IN ENGLAND

Citizens of the twentieth century live in a time of tremendous complexities. To understand this technological age in which you live, you must learn something about the early development of industry. Throughout the world and in every country, the modern age of machinery has made a significant impact upon society.

Just as a roaring, sweeping fire can begin with only a few sparks, so was the Industrial Revolution ignited. Events occurring on the continent of Europe during its darkest hours (the Middle Ages) lit the flame of a machine age that has burned steadily ever since.

Section Objectives

Review these objectives. When you have completed this section, you should be able to:

1. List the early European influences that affected the beginning of the Industrial Revolution.

2. Describe the early industrial developments and inventions that advanced industry's growth in Europe and England.

    2.1 List the requirements of an industrial nation.

    2.2 Explain the development of the factory system.

    2.3 Describe the changes induced by the steam engine and other early inventions that increased productivity.

Vocabulary

Study these words to enhance your learning success in this section.

aristocracy	capital	capitalism
capitalist	free enterprise	industrialism
proletariat	sequestered	

Note: *All vocabulary words in this LIFEPAC appear in* boldface *print the first time they are used. If you are not sure of the meaning when you are reading, study the definitions given.*

SPARKS OF PREPARATION

The Industrial Revolution brought about a dramatic change in the production of articles people used, bought, and sold. Instead of depending upon manual labor as his ancestors had done for centuries, man could now produce materials more efficiently by machine. Originating in England in the 1750s, the Industrial Revolution was affected by events that occurred much earlier in mainland Europe. It would be helpful to examine some of these events here.

European background. The Middle Ages in Europe was not known as a period of creative ideas or visionary goals. Life remained stagnant for most people who were caught up in a feudal system that kept the rich wealthy and the poor penniless. During this era, monasteries were established where monks worked, prayed, studied, and lived a very sequestered lifestyle. As monasteries spread throughout Europe, these Catholic centers inadvertently became models for the factories that developed during the Industrial Revolution. The demands of strict discipline and specific work responsibilities were later duplicated in mines, mills, and factories throughout the industrialized world.

| Monasteries are early models of organized labor.

In 1095 Pope Urban II of Rome launched a military movement against the Muslims who occupied Palestine. This military movement was the first of many Crusades to free the Holy Land from the Muslims. Understandably, the Muslims were fierce in their resistance to the Western European invaders, and the Crusaders were unable to hold on to their territorial gains. Something else, however, was captured that in time became even more meaningful. A revival of interest in travel and trade swept over the invading armies. As Italians, Germans, English, French, and other Crusaders passed through the wealthy areas of the Eastern Byzantine Empire, the desire for a better way of life and luxuries increased. Many Italian merchants settled in Constantinople, generating a trade market between eastern and western European countries.

Europe was enthralled by the commodities and attractions of the Eastern culture, and the business eyes of the economically sleepy westerners were reopened. Economic opportunities were now a possibility for which to work and dream.

Other factors paving the way for industrialism included the capitalism of bankers and merchants. These bankers and merchants flourished in Europe at the end of the Middle Ages and continued to grow throughout the Renaissance. The profit motive was a driving force in nations that supported a free enterprise system. Businessmen in Europe became increasingly more aware of opportunities for prosperity as their businesses increased. To increase their trade and commerce, they had to produce more goods. This increase in production required more trained workers. Additional labor at a cheap price was in demand in order to increase profits.

Having had their appetites whetted by the Crusades, the Renaissance, and a spirit of self-improvement, Europe became filled with the excitement of eager travelers. Scores of people journeyed from country to country seeking better occupational opportunities.

England soon led the way in industrial production and management. An indication of the type of success England would experience as an industrial country was evident in the abundance of potential factory labor it attracted.

From the countryside of England, farmers who had been driven from their lands sought work in the urban areas. Many Irish families seeking a better way of life in England's cities left their homelands because of extreme poverty and lack of opportunities.

Besides a strong work force, England also possessed other basic requirements for industrial growth that gave the country an advantage in the Industrial Revolution. English merchants and businessmen had sufficient money and materials to risk in investments to make an eventual profit. Coal, iron, and other raw materials essential for industry were abundant. Good transportation was also available to distribute goods to markets at home and abroad. With so many positive conditions, England's machine age was ready to swing into action, and the stage for England's Industrial Revolution was set.

✎ **Match the following items.**

1.1 _____ Industrial Revolution

1.2 _____ Middle Ages

1.3 _____ Crusades

1.4 _____ profit motive

1.5 _____ free-enterprise system

a. investing at a risk for financial gain

b. change from hand power to machine power

c. businesses competing for profit without undue government intervention

d. system used by monasteries

e. attempts to free the Holy Land from the Muslims

f. European history—from Rome's fall to the Renaissance

Write the letter for the correct answer on each line.

1.6 Patterns monasteries established for helping industry included (1) strict discipline, (2) inventive spirit, (3) specific work responsibilities. _____
   a. 1, 2   b. 2, 3   c. 1, 3   d. 1, 2, and 3

1.7 Effects the Crusades had in sparking the industrial age included (1) revived interest in trade, (2) revived interest in business, (3) increased desire to be prosperous and productive, (4) interest in factory development. _____
   a. 1, 2, 4   b. 2, 3, 4   c. 1, 3, 4   d. 1, 2, 3

1.8 The basic component a nation does not need to become industrialized is _____ .
   a. sufficient manpower   b. natural resources
   c. capital   d. fertile soil

Essential inventions. By allowing one man to do the same amount of work that once required many men to do, the inventions of numerous machines greatly enhanced the growth of the Industrial Revolution. In the 1440s a German printer named John Gutenberg invented a press that could print material by using movable type. A book that once would have taken months to write by hand could now be printed in days. The Bible was the first book to be printed on Gutenberg's press, making it readily available and affordable by even the common man.

The influence of the printing press was tremendous prior to the growth of the Industrial Revolution. An astute businessman could easily see the potential profit to be made by switching to machinery from manual labor. Once the print was set properly, copies could be quickly run off, thereby eliminating endless hours of painstaking hand copying.

Historians generally agree that, although its roots reached back into the Middle Ages, the Industrial Revolution did not actually begin until after 1750. Inventions created after that date were largely responsible for fanning the sparks in England's flaming revolution. Those inventions soon spread throughout Europe and westerly across the Atlantic Ocean.

The drastic changes brought about by industrialization were first felt in England's growing textile industry. The manufacturing of cotton cloth, for example, was a decided improvement over the tedious work done by a seamstress in shops or within homes.

English businessmen imported the raw cotton that was to be woven into cloth by the spinsters and the weavers who worked in the textile mills. Since demand for cotton cloth was high, more efficient methods were needed in its production. John Kay invented the flying shuttle in 1733, and this invention sped up the weaving process considerably. An improvement of the weaving loom, the flying shuttle allowed the pull of a cord to move a shuttle back and forth over thread that formerly had to be pushed by hand. As expected, the flying shuttle greatly increased production of cloth.

Following John Kay's invention came the demand for more efficient spinning wheels to make the thread needed for weaving. To meet this demand, James Hargreaves invented the spinning jenny in 1764. This new machine could spin eight times as much thread as the previous single spinning wheels.

Both the flying shuttle and the spinning jenny were improved and eventually were replaced by better machines. Both of these inventions led to a dramatic change in England's economy.

The selling price of cotton cloth went down as it became cheaper to produce. Consequently, the price reduction increased the demand for the cloth. In turn, an increase in demand for more cloth created a demand for more raw cotton. The invention of a cotton gin helped to meet those demands. Eli Whitney, a colonial school teacher and gunmaker from Connecticut who later relocated in Savannah, Georgia, experimented with a machine that separated cotton seeds from the lint. In 1793 Whitney succeeded in perfecting the cotton gin. This invention meant that instead of one man separating one pound of cotton per day, he could separate *fifty* pounds in the same length of time. Therefore, the cotton gin boosted efficiency and production within the textile industry.

Great technological strides were also being made in England's iron and steel industry. The two raw materials needed by this industry were coal and iron. By the eighteenth century, improvements in the iron industry allowed England to produce a better quality of iron. This improvement resulted largely from the development of a hotter fire by using coke (coal that had been heated to remove certain impurities). The blast furnace was developed after the discovery that blasting air through coke produced a greater heat. The burning of certain gases in the production of coke was used in making light and heat, thus increasing the fire's intensity. Later, steel was also developed by taking impurities out of the iron and adding certain minerals. Steel, a lighter metal, expanded the variety of products available and increased the efficiency of metal at the same time.

As England's Industrial Revolution progressed, additional industries were developed. For example, one new industry centered around the production of rubber. During the eighteenth century, the people of Europe used rubber for pencil erasers, shoes, and coats. Rubber was brought to Europe from the West Indies by Columbus.

So many inventions and new technological developments in the economy explain why the Industrial Revolution accelerated. The changes brought about by the Industrial Revolution were innumerable. As the demand increased, the supply of these products increased accordingly.

New methods of business organization and operation also developed, increasing production and efficiency. Within a few years, the switch from hand power to machine power had drastically changed life for the people. However, the Industrial Revolution had only begun.

Match the inventors with their inventions.

1.9 _____ Gutenberg

1.10 _____ Kay

1.11 _____ Hargreaves

1.12 _____ Whitney

a. spinning jenny

b. printing press

c. spinning wheel

d. cotton gin

e. flying shuttles

Complete the following activities.

1.13 Describe the improvements brought about in the iron industry by the following developments.

a. coke _____

b. blast furnace _____

c. steel _____

1.14 Give three changes brought about by the Industrial Revolution.

a. _____

b. _____

c. _____

1.15 As an eighteenth-century textile company manager, describe the influences and changes brought about by Kay, Hargreaves, and Whitney on your business. Compare your answer with that of a friend.

_____

_____

_____

_____

_____

_____

TEACHER CHECK _____ _____

initials   date

FIRES OF CONTINUATION

Before the Industrial Revolution, work was conducted mainly at home or in a nearby workshop. Setting his own hours, a man could work at a pace best suited for him, his family, and his customers. The tools he used were his own. The food for his family was grown in the family garden. The preindustrial worker was largely independent and self-sufficient.

The Industrial Revolution greatly altered lifestyles, and the development of the factory system created potential for new energy sources.

Development of the factory system. The shift to manufacturing brought dramatic changes in working conditions. Machines became too large and too expensive to maintain at home; therefore, they were kept in a large building or in a group of buildings. These business centers, or factories, were initially located where water power was available to run the machines. These new factories exerted pressure on the working man. The worker often had to either travel great distances to work or relocate near the factory.

The setting up of a factory involved a great deal of money. Although certain individuals were able to accumulate enough money to become factory owners, they were the exception rather than the norm. Therefore, several businesses often combined to gather sufficient **capital**. In such cases people individually bought shares of stock, enabling them to become part owners of the new establishment. Depending upon the number of shares owned, each stockholder would then receive a percentage of the business's profits.

The number of **capitalists** who were willing to invest large amounts of money continued to increase in England. The financial backing of industry demanded tremendous amounts of capital to operate huge factories. Financial support came from merchants who had become wealthy through trading during previous years.

| Early factory workers

Most of these merchants were middle-class citizens. The upper class, which consisted of the nobility and the **aristocracy**, made their fortunes by owning land. The idea of involving themselves in such mundane things as machines and factories was unthinkable! When the middle class gained enough wealth and power in business to strongly influence the country, however, the upper class quickly changed their way of thinking.

Factories, by their very nature, categorized people into two groups—those directing the work and those performing the assigned tasks. Although both groups were employed by the same company, they held positions of varying responsibilities.

The group that directed or administered the work was paid a monthly or yearly salary. The workers, or **proletariat**, carried out the orders in exchange for their daily or weekly earnings (wages). These workers bore the burden of the factory system whereas the owners and, to a lesser extent, the administrators reaped the benefits. Many workers owned little other than the clothes on their backs, and they worked under conditions that bordered on slavery. Beggars, street people, women, and children were among the original factory workers. These people were soon joined by skilled workers. Many farmers and artisans were drawn helplessly into the factory system as their occupations faltered. Spinners, weavers, shoemakers, and tailors, among others, entered a new vocation where their treasured skills were deemed worthless. Although some skilled workers managed to remain independent, many workers fell slave to the factory system.

In spite of the many negative aspects, factories did offer various positive advantages. For example, they provided needed jobs for many of the unemployed and gradually improved economic conditions within the nation. Industries, through good performance, contributed their share in balancing employment, trade, and commerce both nationally and internationally.

Unfortunately, in the eyes of the capitalists, the poor conditions created by the factory system were of little interest. The factory system did not concern itself with the needs of individuals but demanded performance even at a personal price. In thinking only of monetary gain, industry exacted a heavy toll from its workers and their families. The primary importance of a God-created individual (Genesis 1:27) was largely ignored. Consequently, self-esteem and dignity were crushed. Placed on an assembly line, men found their creativity, dignity, and sense of worth stifled by machine-like motions. The well-being of the common man was sacrificed to allow for increases in production, distribution, and efficiency.

 Write the letter or letters for the correct answer on each line.

1.16 Before the Industrial Revolution, craftsmen _____ .

    a. set their own hours

    c. owned their trade

    b. traded their products for food

    d. ran their business at home

1.17 Stockholders in large businesses _____ .

    a. became part owners

    c. decided company policies

    b. received a share of the profits

    d. lost when the company lost

1.18 Positions in factories included _____ .

    a. assembly-line workers

    c. administrators

    b. owners

    d. stocks

1.19 The following groups of people became factory workers: _____ .

    a. farmers

    c. skilled artisans

    b. women and children

    d. owners

1.20 Positive advantages of the machine age were _____ .

    a. that it supplied jobs

    c. better working conditions

    b. that it improved the economy

    d. that it increased production

1.21 The factory worker bore the brunt of the factory system through the stifling of his _____ .

    a. self-worth   b. creativity

    c. assembly-line job   d. dignity

Answer each question.

1.22 Why did businesses switch from homes to factories? _____

_____

_____

1.23 How could a businessman without sufficient capital to start his own factory still become part

    of a large company? _____

_____

_____

_____

1.24 Imagine you are a shoemaker-turned-factory worker. To what degree has your self-image

    and lifestyle changed? Explain. _____

_____

_____

_____

_____

Potential for energy sources. The power of the machine made the industrial age awesome. Physically strong men were no match for the power of machines in industry. As automatic machines came into their own, their power potential greatly increased. Early factories were located along rivers, streams, and waterfalls that provided the power necessary to run the machines.

As the Industrial Revolution strengthened and progressed, so did the power behind it. An advancement in the use of water-driven machines was that of heated water or steam. Although Hero, a scientist who lived in Alexandria, Egypt, described and built the first known steam engine as early as 120 B.C., the English were given the real credit for the invention. In 1698 Thomas Savery developed the first practical steam engine, a pump to drain water from mines. In 1712 Thomas Newcome improved upon Savery's steam engine. Steam power, however, did not become popular until James Watt patented an advanced steam engine in 1769. The uniqueness of Watt's engine was its ability to drive other machines. This new power source enabled factories engaged in spinning and weaving to be located away from water sources.

Besides the tremendous benefits to operating factory machines, steam power also made its influence felt in the field of transportation. Railroads and steamships were actually revolutions of their own in transportation, constantly improving on speed, comfort, and safety. With the advent of the steam engine, more people were able to afford travel. Businessmen benefited from the steam engine's transportation modes in their trading, buying, and selling ventures. Better transportation no longer placed businessmen at the mercy of the deplorable road systems.

During the early days of the Industrial Revolution, most roads were barely passable. Roads were heavily rutted trails, dusty during dry weather and muddy when it rained. Heavy loads were carried by mules and packhorses at an extremely slow pace. Forty to fifty miles a day was the average amount of traveling a person could tolerate along these poor routes.

Finding a solution to this deplorable situation, John McAdam of Scotland constructed a new, improved road. McAdam used large stones as a foundation for the road and covered them with layers of smaller stones. The top layer was composed of still smaller stones held together with mud. Finally, a large roller pressed the surface, making it smooth for travel. The difference was incredible and greatly improved road travel. With the exception of mud to hold the stones together, modern roads today are constructed in much the same manner. With these new roads, the steam engine-powered industries were no longer hindered by time-consuming delays that cost them precious hours and days in the distribution of their products.

Water travel, also extremely slow, was improved by the steam engine. The endless waiting for winds to move ships along demanded an alternative, and the fast growth of the Industrial Revolution perpetuated such an improvement in water transportation. With these innovations, raw materials could be moved to factories quickly to speed up production. Likewise, manufacturers also benefited from the improved roads and the transportation systems by getting their products out to widespread markets.

In addition, the construction of canals in England, and later in other industrial nations, did much to solve the distribution problem. Although this method of water travel improved transportation conditions, increased speed was the next objective.

Several inventors experimented with the use of the steam engine for water travel, but an American named Robert Fulton was the first to put this high-powered potential to use. Fulton's steamship, the *Clermont*, became famous in the United States and directly influenced

| Steam provides power for the machine age.

transatlantic travel by the steamship. This discovery was a tremendous boost to both European and American industries. It enabled goods to be distributed throughout the world at a faster pace and at a cheaper price than by sailing vessels.

Land travel took a great leap forward in 1814 when the English engineer, George Stephenson, developed a steam locomotive. Running on rails, the locomotive was powered by coal that helped produce steam. Stephenson perfected the engine and by 1830 his steam locomotive, the *Rocket*, pulled railroad cars from Liverpool to Manchester, England, at the amazing speed of twenty-nine miles per hour! Consequently, George Stephenson's locomotive immediately created a world-wide demand for the construction of these steam locomotives. A fast method of transportation, the steam locomotive also proved to be safer than road travel.

Within a relatively few years, the uses of the steam engine had spread from powering factories to driving fast-moving steamships and locomotives. Not only had the steam engine quickened the production processes, but it also enhanced the distribution techniques of materials. The steam engine's power potential and usefulness became almost unlimited in view of the technology and the knowledge with which man has been endowed by his Creator.

Answer true or false.

1.25 _____ Early factories were located by rivers so they could operate by water power.

1.26 _____ Newcome and Watt made improvements in the steam engine.

1.27 _____ The uniqueness of the steam engine was its ability to power-drive other machines.

1.28 _____ Steam engines were used in transportation to build roads and in powering steamships and steam locomotives.

1.29 _____ McAdam developed an improved method of road building.

1.30 _____ Fulton and Stephenson developed steam locomotives.

Write the letter of the correct answer on the line.

1.31 Inventions and methods of the Industrial Revolution in England and Europe did not include

the _____ .

a. steam engine   b. factory system   c. cotton gin
d. printing press   e. flying shuttle   f. steam locomotive

Answer the following questions.

1.32 How did the following inventions or improvements boost industry?

a. steam engine _____

b. improved road building _____

c. steam ship _____

d. steam locomotive _____

1.33 What advantages did the steam-powered factories have over those driven by water power?

Discuss with a friend and record your answer. _____

_____

_____

_____

TEACHER CHECK _____ _____

initials   date

Review the material in this section in preparation for the Self Test. The Self Test will check your mastery of this particular section. The items missed on this Self Test will indicate specific areas where restudy is needed for mastery.

SELF TEST 1

Match these items (each answer, 2 points).

1.01	_____	Gutenberg	a.	flying shuttle
1.02	_____	Watt	b.	steam engine
1.03	_____	McAdam	c.	wars to capture the Holy Land
1.04	_____	Kay	d.	printing press
1.05	_____	Hargreaves	e.	cotton gin
1.06	_____	Fulton	f.	spinning jenny
1.07	_____	Stephenson	g.	*Clermont*
1.08	_____	Crusades	h.	change from hand to machine
1.09	_____	Whitney	i.	*Torch*
1.010	_____	Industrial Revolution	j.	improved road building
			k.	wars of the Industrial Revolution
			l.	*Rocket*

Complete the sentences (each answer, 3 points).

1.011 Europe's dark years under the feudal system are called the _____ .

1.012 Monasteries set an example for factories in a. _____ and b. _____ .

1.013 The Crusades revived Europe's interest in a. _____ and b. _____ .

1.014 Industrialized methods and inventions were used first in England in the _____ _____ industry.

1.015 Two raw materials needed by industry were a. _____ and b. _____ .

1.016 The two groups of factory employees were a. _____ and b. _____ .

1.017 People who individually bought into a corporation were called _____ .

1.018 The disadvantages of factory life were endured largely by the _____ .

1.019 Inventions that developed from the use of the steam engine in transportation were the

a. _____ and b. _____ .

1.020 Factories were first powered by a. _____ then changed to b. _____ .

Answer true or false (each answer, 1 point).

1.021 _____ The Crusades were led by Catholic Turks to free Palestine.

1.022 _____ The production of goods by trained workers was necessary for trade to increase.

1.023 _____ The Bible was the first book to be printed on Hargreaves' press.

1.024 _____ The Industrial Revolution really began in England after 1750.

1.025 _____ Kay's and Hargreaves' inventions increased textile production.

1.026 _____ Before the Industrial Revolution, craftsmen commonly worked at home.

1.027 _____ Factory workers were unskilled laborers.

1.028 _____ The *Clermont* and the *Rocket* were driven by wind power.

1.029 _____ The steamship ended delays in water travel.

1.030 _____ Steam locomotives provided a faster and safer means of transporting goods.

Write the letter of the correct answer on each line (each answer, 2 points).

1.031 The basic requirements needed by a nation for industrial growth are (1) work force, (2) corporations, (3) natural resources, (4) sufficient capital. _____

    a. 1, 2, 3   b. 2, 3, 4   c. 1, 2, 4   d. 1, 3, 4

1.032 Early factors influencing the Industrial Revolution included (1) feudal system, (2) Crusades, (3) monasteries, (4) capitalism of bankers. _____

    a. 1, 2, 3   b. 2, 3, 4   c. 1, 2, 4   d. 1, 3, 4

1.033 Changes brought about by the Industrial Revolution included (1) increased production, (2) slower distribution, (3) cheaper goods, (4) better products. _____

    a. 1, 2, 3   b. 2, 3, 4   c. 1, 3, 4   d. 1, 2, 4

1.034 The age of the machine (1) decreased unemployment, (2) improved the economy, (3) concerned itself with individuals, (4) stifled the common man. _____

    a. 1, 2, 3   b. 2, 3, 4   c. 1, 2, 4   d. 1, 3, 4

1.035 Practical uses of the steam engine included (1) improving roads, (2) running factories (3) steamships, (4) steam locomotives. _____

    a. 2, 3, 4   b. 1, 2, 3   c. 1, 3, 4   d. 1, 2, 4

Answer the following questions (each answer, 4 points).

1.036 What industrial advantages enabled England to lead the way in Europe's Industrial

Revolution? _____

_____

_____

1.037 What improvements did the Industrial Revolution bring to the textile and the iron industries?

a. _____

_____

b. _____

_____

1.038 How were factories established? _____

_____

_____

1.039 What advantages did the steam engine bring to industry? _____

_____

_____

_____

2. INDUSTRIAL REVOLUTION IN THE UNITED STATES

Several European countries, England in particular, possessed favorable conditions for the growth of the Industrial Revolution. None of these countries, however, had the overwhelming abundance and availability of resources and labor for industrial growth as did the United States. Consequently, when the Industrial Revolution crossed the Atlantic, the setting and timing were exceedingly favorable for the machine age in the United States. This section of the LIFEPAC deals with the early growing pains of industry in the United States to its inevitable advancement in mass production, transportation, and communication.

Section Objectives

Review these objectives. When you have completed this section, you should be able to:

3. List the factors that made the early United States ripe for industry.

   3.1 List the advantages available in the United States for industrial growth.

   3.2 List the early inventions in agriculture, transportation, and communication.

4. Explain the influence of wars on industry and the effects of industry on war.

5. Describe the advantages and disadvantages of the growth and influence of corporations on the economy.

6. List the technological developments that greatly increased United States productivity.

   6.1 Explain the new methods of mass production.

   6.2 Describe the effects new inventions in transportation, communication, and energy had on industry.

Vocabulary

Study these words to enhance your learning success in this section.

consolidation   mobilized   monopoly   standardized

UNITED STATES INDUSTRIAL CLIMATE

With the arrival of the Industrial Revolution in the United States, the steady tapping of this nation's natural resources began. The seemingly limitless supply of energy-producing products gave the machine-oriented movement a gigantic surge that even England could not equal.

Early United States setting. Coal was a necessary source for powering factories. Coal rested beneath the fertile soil of the Appalachian states in the East. This enormous energy source, as well as many powerful rivers and streams, lay untapped. The rich land and mild climate of the South was ideal for large scale agriculture. The vast American continent was rich in minerals to be mined and in fish and wild game to feed a growing nation.

Unlike England and Europe, the United States had a continuous supply of potential factory workers seeking citizenship in this country. Some farmers, artisans, and skilled workers entered industry, but many of these people preferred other occupations. With more economic opportunities available than those offered by England and Europe, factory work was not the only employment alternative open to people in the United States. Since many of the immigrants were largely untrained, the factory setting was the only option. Although conditions under industrial management were often harsh, many of these new citizens were grateful just to have a job.

Capital was the essential ingredient that made all the natural resources, workers, and machines work smoothly to create an industrialized nation. To accomplish this work, businessmen would have to combine their financial resources in order for industry to develop to its potential in the United States. The United States had a number of wealthy businessmen who were willing to invest their money. New England investors, in particular, were interested in the development of American industry.

These businessmen were encouraged by their observations of what the Industrial Revolution had done, and was doing, in England and in other parts of Europe. Taking into account the positive climate of industry in the United States and motivated by the hope of large profits, businessmen eagerly invested their funds. Most of this capital from northeastern investors had been acquired from prior successful shipbuilding and trading ventures. Now these businessmen had an opportunity to put their profits back to work in their homeland.

A strong feeling of resentment toward England and a desire to excel, especially by New Englanders following the Revolutionary War, was an additional motivation behind the growth of the Industrial Revolution in this country. Feelings between the two countries were still touchy, and England reluctantly shared its machine technology with its former colonies. The desire of the United States to remove the stigma of being a second-rate or lesser nation was another strong drive in its determination to succeed in the age of industry.

Blessed with an abundant supply of natural resources, workers, and capital, the United States was equipped to embark upon the industrial age. Little did the United States, or the rest of the world, imagine that someday this young nation would grow into the world's most powerful industrial nation.

Answer true or false.

2.1 _____ England was the leading European industrial nation in the 1700s.

2.2 _____ Immigrants in the United States supplied a large amount of the working force in factories.

2.3 _____ Money for American industry was supplied by southern plantation owners.

2.4 _____ Natural resources are the main ingredient for beginning industry.

2.5 _____ New Englanders grew wealthy from shipbuilding and trading.

Answer the following questions.

2.6 What natural resources in the United States made it ripe for industry's growth?

_____

2.7 Imagine you are a wealthy New England businessman in the late 1700s. Why are you willing to invest your assets at a risk in beginning American industry?

_____

_____

_____

Early industrial accomplishments. While taking advantage of the industrial inventions and improvements that had revolutionized England and Europe, people in the United States were working hard on inventions and technology of their own. The United States' most valuable invention of the eighteenth century was developed by Eli Whitney in 1793. Whitney's cotton gin was to become one of the most potent forces behind the machine-produced agricultural revolution in the United States. Although the cotton gin did not decrease the demand for slaves in the South, agriculture could now enjoy the advantage that machine labor had over manual labor.

The cotton gin was only the first in a procession of labor-saving machines that boosted the agricultural revolution in the United States. In 1819, Jethro Wood developed the iron plow, thereby replacing the traditional wooden plow. Fifty years later the iron plow was upgraded by James Oliver's steel plow that was much lighter to handle and more efficient. An additional boost to the agricultural industry came in 1834 when Cyrus McCormick invented the reaping machine. Eliminating the slow process of cutting grain by hand, the reaper improved the quality and the quantity of production and saved the farmers valuable time. The development of the threshing machine in 1836 that separated the grain from the chaff also eliminated much time consuming work for the farmer. The change from manual labor to machinery revolutionized agriculture.

The Industrial Revolution began in this country during the administration of President Thomas Jefferson. Expensive international trade and commerce was slow in coming to industry in the United States. For example, trade with Europe was hindered because of a war between England and France, and the *Embargo Act of 1807* prevented United States' ships from sailing to England with goods to sell and to trade. The sudden absence of English trade, however, caused a formerly dependent nation to begin to manufacture goods at home. As a result, this embargo forced the United States to become more self-reliant by creating its own improvements and by fostering trade internally with its own people. Subsequently, competition among businessmen increased and became a motivating factor that greatly accelerated productivity throughout industry in this country.

During this period, increased manufacturing in the United States occurred primarily in the textile, iron, and leather industries. Demand for more goods prompted the demand for better transportation by which to distribute the produced goods to consumers. Unfortunately, the dirt roads in the United States were deeply rutted, dusty, frequently muddy, dangerous, and unsafe for travel. In 1811 construction began on a national road to help alleviate some of these transportation problems. Starting in Cumberland, Maryland, the road's initial destination was Wheeling, Virginia, which is now in West Virginia. This road, known as the *Cumberland Road*, was thirty to eighty feet wide and was covered with crushed rock. It was a major improvement to the usual hazardous routes of this era. The *Cumberland Road* was traveled by farmers, cattlemen, sheepherders, and traders. In addition to its use in the distribution of manufactured goods, stagecoaches, mail deliveries, and covered Conestoga wagons heading West used the new highway, which was a safer, quicker, and more comfortable route for travelers. Other roads in the country were later patterned after the *Cumberland Road*.

Industry also needed improved and expanded water routes in the United States. Canals were constructed in many areas, providing a cheaper method of transporting goods. In 1825 the Erie Canal was completed, connecting Lake Erie with New York's Hudson River. The Erie Canal created a direct route from the Great Lakes to the Atlantic Ocean. The cost of shipping grain from Buffalo to New York City dropped from $100 to $5 per ton. Many middle westerners took advantage of this inexpensive way of transporting products to eastern markets. Following the success of the Erie, other canals were built between Philadelphia and Pittsburgh, the Ohio River and Lake Erie, Lake Michigan and the Illinois River, and Lake Champlain and the Hudson River. This construction of waterways aided the overall economy, travel, and recreation of this nation as well as boosting industry.

Enhancing river transportation even further, Robert Fulton developed the steamboat in 1807, revolutionizing water travel. Launching his *Clermont* for a round trip of three hundred miles from New York City to Albany, Fulton soon put a stop to such disparaging remarks as "Fulton's Folly." Fulton's successful voyage created immense interest in the advantages of the steamship. Soon cities such as St. Louis, Cincinnati, Louisville, and New Orleans used steamships frequently for travel on the Ohio and the Mississippi Rivers.

Water travel and the steamship, however, could not keep pace with the demand for improved land transportation. The lack of water in key agricultural and industrial areas led to another popular use of the steam engine, the locomotive. Steam locomotives became known as the backbone of industry in the United States. Their value became apparent following the building of the locomotive called the *Tom Thumb* in 1830 by Peter Cooper. Older locomotives, driven by horses along tracks, quickly gave way to the new improved steam versions. At the time of Cooper's model, only thirty miles of railroad track had been laid in the United States. By 1840 track mileage had increased to 2,800 miles, and by 1860 the nation had 30,000 miles of track traversing the country. Besides the obvious advantages of improved speed and

| Transportation improvements

efficiency in the transportation of goods, mail, and passengers, the railroad also boosted the iron and steel industries. A staggering three hundred tons of iron and steel were necessary to build a single mile of track!

Industrial accomplishments were also changing the textile field. In the early 1800s, Francis C. Lowell built a clothing factory in Massachusetts where raw cotton was made into cloth. By producing cotton cloth in such large quantities, prices could be set much lower, providing a much greater availability of cotton goods. Facilitating the production of cloth even more was the invention of the sewing machine by Elias Howe in 1846. The sewing machine eliminated the slow, tedious process of making clothing by hand. It also brought further reduction in clothing prices, thus making cotton garments available to people who had little money to spend.

Consequently, industry began to affect all areas and walks of life in the United States. In a few short years, industry in this country had taken on new dimensions. Great strides had been gained in the production and distribution of goods. Factories were producing better products in greater quantities; farms were producing larger crops with less labor; and transportation of manufactured and processed goods was quicker, safer, and more economical. Clearly the United States was well on its way to becoming a powerful industrial nation.

Match following inventors with their inventions.

2.8	_____ Whitney	a.	steam locomotive
2.9	_____ Wood	b.	reaping machine
2.10	_____ Oliver	c.	cotton cloth factory
2.11	_____ McCormick	d.	steamboat
2.12	_____ Fulton	e.	threshing machine
2.13	_____ Cooper	f.	cotton gin
2.14	_____ Lowell	g.	steel plow
		h.	iron plow

Answer true or false.

2.15 _____ The first national road was called the Cumberland Road.

2.16 _____ The United States' first canal connected Lake Erie with the Ohio River.

2.17 _____ The Embargo Act reduced production in the United States.

2.18 _____ "Fulton's Folly," the *Clermont*, was a steamboat.

2.19 _____ The railroad industry boosted the iron and steel industries.

Answer each question.

2.20 What inventions and improvements affected the following industries in the United States?

a. agricultural _____

b. textile _____

c. transportation _____

d. iron and steel _____

2.21 What advantages were provided to industry by the following developments?

a. the Embargo Act of 1807 _____

b. the Cumberland Road _____

c. the *Clermont* _____

d. the *Tom Thumb* _____

e. the Erie Canal _____

f. the thresher and the reaper _____

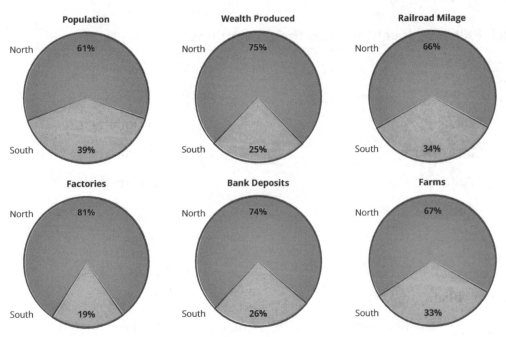

Comparison of North and South in 1860

RISE OF INDUSTRIAL PROGRESS

Not only did technological production developments add to the growth and expansion of industry in the United States, but the wars fought at home and abroad directly influenced industry's progress in the United States.

Advantage of war. With all its destruction, grief, and heartache, war does have some advantages, especially for those involved in industry. Industry does not consider war from a moral standpoint but rather from a monetary one. England and other European countries had already learned from experience that the production of bullets, cannon balls, warships, and similar military equipment kept factories busy and profits high. Industry boomed continuously and rapidly in preparation for war. In addition, as soldiers were mobilized for war, jobs were left vacant for others. Not only did unemployment decrease, but workers were also called upon to work extra hours to meet war's surging production demands.

When the War of 1812 broke out, the United States met the initial test in its ability to produce war supplies and equipment on an immediate, demanding basis. An important pattern was being established for the United States' future war production and defense purposes. Congress put war supplies high on its list of priorities in the nation's defense against England and Canada during this conflict. Although little ground was claimed by the United States in Canada, the military was successful in driving off British ships in sea battles.

The United States asserted itself militarily on land also. In the battle of New Orleans in 1815, General Andrew Jackson and his men faced a force of some five thousand British soldiers who marched against the Americans in straight lines on the open field. Jackson's troops, however, fought from behind barricades and embankments, killing over two thousand British soldiers while losing only about seventy men.

The humiliating British loss actually occurred after the war between the United States and the former mother country had officially ended. Thus, the War of 1812 gave the United States and its industry international respect, boosting its ambitions for a prominent position in world trade and commerce.

Approximately fifty years later, this nation was engaged in the most tragic conflict of all times— the Civil War. The industrialized North was too well equipped for the agricultural South. Between 1820 and 1860, the majority of the factory workers were located in the Northern industrial sections of the United States. The Southern economy, on the other hand, was basically centered around an agricultural lifestyle. As a result, the North would eventually defeat the determined but under-equipped South.

The fighting lasted four long years, ending in victory for the North; but, more importantly, it succeeded in preserving the Union. The gallant fighting spirit, morale, and sectional loyalty of the South was eventually worn down by the industrially backed federal troops. The determining factor in the Northern victory was the strength of its industry.

War tactics in the Civil War were altered by industrialization. Both the Northern and Southern armies took advantage of the mobility provided by the steamboat and railroad. Fierce, bloody battles were fought for control of these important modes of transportation.

The recently developed method of electrical telegraph communication was also widely used and perfected. The telegraph, invented by Samuel F. B. Morse in 1844, swiftly transmitted warfare communications by electricity. The telegraph system was a dramatic improvement over the relay riders on horseback. Assembly line production of war arms and equipment in the North brought speedy replacement of weapons and other necessities of war.

The modern age of warfare had arrived, and victory depended largely upon the strength and backing of industry. Wars have few advantages, but the War of 1812 and the Civil War gave the youthful United States' industry a boost into maturity. The groundwork had been laid for future growth and development that would transform this country into a powerful nation.

 Write the letter of the correct answer on each line.

2.22 Wars brought (1) increased production, (2) fewer jobs, (3) decreased unemployment, (4) growth to industry. _____
   a. 1, 2, 3   b. 2, 3, 4   c. 1, 3, 4   d. 1, 2, 4

2.23 Wars that matured American industry included (1) War of 1812, (2) Civil War, (3) American Revolution, (4) Spanish-American War. _____
   a. 1, 2, 3   b. 2, 3, 4   c. 1, 3, 4   d. 1, 2

2.24 Industrial developments influencing the Civil War included (1) the steamboat, (2) an assembly-line production, (3) the telephone, (4) the telegraph. _____
   a. 1, 2, 4   b. 1, 2, 3   c. 2, 3, 4   d. 1, 3, 4

2.25 The War of 1812 (1) was fought with England, (2) gave America international respect, (3) gained little land, (4) decreased American world trade. _____
   a. 1, 2, 4   b. 1, 2, 3   c. 2, 3, 4   d. 1, 3, 4

Answer the following questions.

2.26 What gave the North an overall advantage in the Civil War? Explain. _____

_____

_____

2.27 What influence did war have on United States industry? _____

_____

_____

_____

2.28 What influence did industry have on wars? _____

_____

_____

Profits of mass production. The United States adjusted to the changes brought about by the daily inventions of those labor-saving devices that replaced muscle power with machine power. In addition, new methods of production were needed to meet the increasing demand for manufactured goods. The United States' market required increased availability of goods at reduced prices with quicker production methods.

Eli Whitney, the inventor of the cotton gin, also originated a system of standardized parts to help meet the demands of industry. As a gun maker in New England, Whitney had made thousands of gun parts so uniformly that they could be used interchangeably. Therefore, if a gun part was lost or worn out, it could easily be replaced by an exact replica instead of making it necessary to purchase a new gun. Whitney's parts idea greatly facilitated production and soon spread to other businesses until the system was installed by all modern age manufacturers.

Even more vital to the growth of mass production was Henry Ford's concept of an assembly-line method of production. In his automobile industry, Ford combined Whitney's system of interchangeable parts with his own creation of the moving assembly line. On the assembly line, Ford's cars were passed along to each worker who installed a certain part. The car then proceeded to other workers until the entire car was completely assembled. This method of car production, compared to earlier methods of constructing one car at a time, also reduced the cost per unit. Thus, the price of a car came within reach of the average person, not just the wealthy.

Production methods such as Whitney's and Ford's systems contributed greatly to the growth of the United States as an industrialized nation. Between the years 1860 and 1894, this nation advanced from fourth to first place among industrialized nations of the world. Railroads, factories, and lumber mills contributed largely to this advancement. Agriculture, once unopposed as the most important business in the United States, was rapidly being replaced by the wheels of industry.

By the late 1800s the industrial strongholds of the United States were centered mainly around the northern portions of the country. The South, once a thriving agricultural economy, fell far behind the North in production following the Civil War. The conflict had been devastating to the Southern economy. Although the South had all the necessary raw materials, manpower, and experience for industry's success, it lacked the capital to back large-scale industry after the war.

By the early 1900s the United States' two leading regions of production were the Middle Atlantic States of New York, New Jersey, and Pennsylvania and the North Central States of Ohio, Indiana, Illinois, Michigan, and Wisconsin. Even the New England States that had enjoyed profitable industry since colonial days could not keep pace with the growth of these high production areas.

The four leading industries producing this tremendous output were food products, textiles, iron and steel, and lumber materials. Ranking first, the major food manufacturers included flour milling, meat packing, sugar refining, and canned and preserved food processing. Employing more workers than the food industries, the United States textile industry was exporting millions of dollars worth of cotton goods by World War I. Basic to all other industry, the iron and steel industry had been aided by the discovery of steel, a tougher, more versatile metal than cast iron. Abundant and relatively inexpensive, steel provided an excellent structural material; therefore, steel was a prime factor in ushering in the modern age of industry. Used in the construction of factory equipment, rails, locomotives, ships, automobiles, bridges, and buildings, steel's industrial output seemed unending and its uses unlimited. To keep pace with the demand, steel was produced by the millions of tons each year.

In view of newer and quicker methods of mass production, the United States' industrial forecast looked exceptionally bright at the beginning of the twentieth century. Manufacturing quality products that were available at lower prices, industry had achieved an amazing degree of progress. The wheels of industry, however, had just begun to turn.

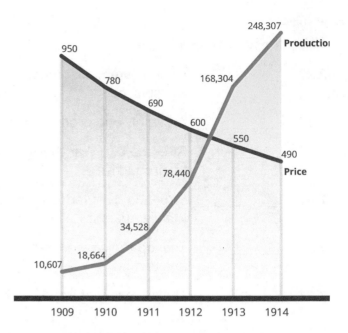

Model-T Mass production
as production goes up, prices go down

Answer true or false.

2.29 _____ Ford's system of standardized parts allowed only the broken or worn parts to be replaced.

2.30 _____ Assembly-line production dropped the cost per unit drastically.

2.31 _____ After the Civil War the Southern economy lacked sufficient raw materials to be productive.

2.32 _____ Strongholds of industry in the North were located in the North Central and Middle Atlantic states.

2.33 _____ The top ranking industries in the United States by 1914 were food products and textiles.

2.34 _____ The discovery of iron soon replaced steel as a structural material.

Give the influence of the following developments on the factory system.

2.35 interchangeable parts _____

_____

2.36 assembly-line production _____

_____

2.37 discovery of steel _____

_____

HISTORY & GEOGRAPHY 1007

LIFEPAC TEST

NAME _____

DATE _____

SCORE _____

HISTORY & GEOGRAPHY 1007: LIFEPAC TEST

Match the following items (each answer, 2 points).

1. _____ Marx   a. telephone

2. _____ Smith   b. steam engine

3. _____ Whitney   c. printing press

4. _____ Ford   d. light bulb

5. _____ McAdam   e. airplane

6. _____ Fulton   f. standardized parts

7. _____ Watt   g. oil well

8. _____ Gutenberg   h. *Communist Manifesto*

9. _____ Edison   i. telegraph

10. _____ Field   j. assembly-line production

11. _____ Oliver   k. steamboat

12. _____ Drake   l. iron plow

13. _____ Bell   m. laissez-faire

14. _____ Morse   n. transatlantic cable

15. _____ Wright   o. steel plow

                      p. reaping machine

                      q. improved road construction

Complete the following sentences (each answer, 3 points).

16. The mass movement of people to the cities was called _____ .

17. Collective or government ownership of production and distribution is _____ .

18. Laissez-faire attitudes opposed government intervention in _____ .

19. The freedom of private business to operate competitively for profit is called the _____ _____ system.

20. The economic system that advocates private ownership and competitive distribution of goods in a free market is called _____ .

21. Negotiations between labor and management are called _____ .

22. The change from hand labor to machine brought about the _____ .

23. The merging of several businesses into one is called _____ .

24. Ford's assembly-line production greatly _____ the cost per unit.

25. The exclusive control of a product by a business is known as a _____ .

26. People who invest their money in a corporation in hopes of sharing in the profits are called
_____ .

Answer true or false (each answer, 1 point).

27. _____ The Crusades revived interest in trade and business in Europe.

28. _____ Monasteries established an early example in discipline and specific work responsibilities for the coming industry.

29. _____ Southern plantation owners invested heavily in early industry in the United States.

30. _____ Not only did war aid industry's growth, but industry also aided war.

31. _____ Industry is usually the deciding factor in a victorious outcome in war.

32. _____ Urbanization and tenement living were two social results of the Industrial Revolution.

33. _____ The inventions of Whitney, McCormick, and Oliver brought about the Agricultural Revolution in the U.S.

Write the letter for the correct answer on each line (each answer, 2 points).

34. The basic requirements needed by a nation for industrial growth are (1) raw materials, (2) work force, (3) capital, (4) trusts. _____
    a. 1, 2, 3   b. 2, 3, 4   c. 1, 2, 4   d. 1, 3, 4

35. Early American industry was given a boost by (1) war, (2) transportation and communication improvements, (3) new power sources, (4) mass production methods, (5) monopolies. _____
    a. 1, 2, 3, 5   b. 2, 3, 4,   c. 1, 2, 3, 4, 5   d. 1, 3, 4, 5

36. Corporations aided the United States' economy by (1) lowering unemployment, (2) setting working and living conditions, (3) better quality products, (4) larger variety of merchandise, (5) lowering prices. _____
    a. 1, 2, 3, 4   b. 1, 3, 4, 5   c. 2, 3, 4, 5   d. 1, 2, 4, 5

37. Factors improving the conditions of factory workers included (1) child labor laws, (2) laissez-faire, (3) labor unions, (4) writings of Dickens and Disraeli, (5) collective bargaining. _____

    a. 1, 2, 3, 4   b. 1, 2, 4, 5   c. 2, 3, 4, 5   d. 1, 3, 4, 5

38. Inventions and developments of the Industrial Revolution in England and Europe included (1) flying shuttle, (2) cotton gin, (3) spinning jenny, (4) printing press, (5) factory system, (6) labor laws. _____

    a. 1, 2, 3, 4, 5   b. 2, 3, 4, 5,6   c. 1, 3, 4, 5, 6   d. 1, 2, 3, 5, 6

Answer the following questions (each answer, 3 points).

39. How did the Industrial Revolution affect

    a. the world economy? _____

    b. production? _____

    c. distribution? _____

    d. trade? _____

    e. the standard of living? _____

40. What changes did the Industrial Revolution bring to the average farmer-turned factory worker?

_____

_____

_____

OTHER INDUSTRIAL DEVELOPMENTS

Besides the accomplishments in production methods to increase the United States' industrial potential, new and improved technological developments were made in transportation, communication, and power sources. Always vital to the success of industry in the United States was the energy that powered it as well as the fact that energy was also being constantly upgraded. Furthermore, this industrial potential and growth led to the development of corporations.

Potential of developed technology. Edwin L. Drake drilled the nation's first oil well in 1859 near Titusville, Pennsylvania, making a new source of power available that had a vast potential. Sarcastically labeled *Drake's Folly* by doubtful onlookers, the *Black Gold* soon gave birth to a new industry. Although first used to make machine parts run smoothly or to light kerosene lamps, oil later became a vital source of power for industry in the United States. In many factories, fuel oil refined from crude oil was used instead of coal to produce steam. Another crude oil product, gasoline, was later used in the newly developed internal combustion engine.

Electricity, already used in communication devices, provided yet another new source of power that would become man's greatest mechanical servant. Thomas A. Edison wanted to create a lamp that would become luminous when electricity passed through it. After attempting to light a lamp with many different filaments, Edison finally succeeded in October of 1879. Edison's light bulb that used a charred cotton thread glowed for forty hours. Edison's dream expanded three years later when he turned the electric power on in a section of New York City, lighting up homes and streets with electric lamps. The advantage to industry was obvious; electricity provided a quick power source that not only would supply light but

would also operate communication systems and power all types of manufacturing equipment at the touch of a fingertip.

Following the development of the internal combustion engine in the 1860s came the invention of the *horseless carriage*—the motor car. The new cylinder engine enabled the designing of successful automobiles by Charles and Frank Duryea, Henry Ford, and Henry Olds. The immense cost of constructing and assembling these transportation masterpieces, however, limited car ownership to the wealthy class. Completely revolutionizing the automobile industry, Henry Ford put his assembly-line production system into action and designed the Model T—the most successful passenger car of its day. Although scoffed at initially, the development of the automobile greatly advanced the transportation system in this country, adding mobility and enrichment to everyday life. A short time later, trucks were designed and soon thereafter buses, more efficient cars, and larger trucks were produced. Consequently, the advantages of these vehicles to industry were many, especially in providing faster distribution of products to markets and to remote areas where railroads did not exist.

Perhaps the most incredible invention of all was the airplane. The airplane completely transformed the transportation industry and made highways in the sky. On December 17, 1903, Wilbur and Orville Wright flew the first successful aircraft. This initial venture was followed by years of improvement and experimentation. In 1908 the Wright brothers sold to the United States Army an airplane that was later used for combat in World War I. The aircraft proved to be exceedingly useful in fighting and in spying missions. Since World War I, air travel has made significant strides and has become an invaluable means of transportation to this country's industry. For example, the

| Other industrial developments

airplane has made the distribution of products and the delivery of raw materials possible in a matter of hours instead of days or weeks. Meanwhile, air travel for business or pleasure has become increasingly more favored because of convenience and speed. Joining the remotest areas of our world, air travel has made almost all regions accessible and subsequently has drawn the nations of the world closer together.

Another impetus to business was the expanded and improved United States postal system. In addition, these new services perfected a more efficient delivery. City mail delivery was developed in 1863; special delivery in 1885 (it was discontinued in 1996); and rural free delivery in 1896. As transportation methods improved, mail delivery improved accordingly throughout the nation.

Telegraph lines continued to link our growing nation from coast to coast. The first transcontinental telegraph was completed in 1861. After several attempts failed to join the United States with England by way of the telegraph, the project was commandeered by the determined and able Cyrus W. Field. Refusing to become discouraged by cable breakdowns, Field's dream became a reality in 1866 with a cable that stretched from Newfoundland, Canada, to England. The first transatlantic line lay on the floor of the Atlantic Ocean, protected by strong cables. Incredibly, messages flashed electrically in a matter of minutes between the two nations.

Another pioneer in the field of communication by wire was Alexander Graham Bell. Bell and other scientists attempted to relay the sound of the human voice over a wire. Bell's efforts were successful on March 10, 1876. The very first telephone message to go out on wire was received by Thomas Watson, Bell's assistant. Watson heard Mr. Bell's call, "Mr Watson, come here. I want you." Although the general public was at first very skeptical about this new development, the American Bell Telephone Company was chartered in 1880 and has become an invaluable communications company. Between 1880 and 1902, telephones increased to more than one million in this nation, enabling businessmen and others to contact each other within seconds.

Other inventions saving countless time, money, and labor in the modern age business office included the typewriter, the cash register, and the adding machine. The list continued to grow in the early 1900s because each day new improvements in technology and production methods were added, thereby making possible more efficient, more productive, and more profitable business.

Match the following items.

2.38	_____ Wright	a.	light bulb
2.39	_____ Ford	b.	transatlantic cable
2.40	_____ Edison	c.	oil well
2.41	_____ Field	d.	airplane
2.42	_____ Bell	e.	typewriter
2.43	_____ Olds	f.	Ford's competitor
2.44	_____ Drake	g.	Model T®
		h.	telephone

Write the letter for the correct answer on each line.

2.45 Sources of power in America by the early 1900s included (1) oil, (2) coal, (3) electricity, (4) atomic power, (5) water power. _____
    a. 1, 2, 3, 4   b. 1, 2, 4, 5   c. 1, 2, 3, 5   d. 2, 3, 4, 5

2.46 Improvements in American communication included (1) new postal services, (2) telephone, (3) Drake's Folly, (4) transatlantic cable, (5) transcontinental telegraph. _____
    a. 1, 2, 3, 4   b. 2, 3, 4, 5   c. 1, 2, 3, 5   d. 1, 2, 4, 5

2.47 Uses for electricity included (1) powered communication systems, (2) lighting, (3) powered machines, (4) _Clermont._ _____
    a. 1, 2, 3   b. 2, 3, 4   c. 1, 3, 4   d. 1, 2, 4

Answer the following question.

2.48 How did the new developments in transportation and communication further the spread of

God's work on earth? _____

_____

_____

_____

_____

_____

TEACHER CHECK _____ _____

initials   date

Growth of corporations. Industry, by its very nature, creates big business. Small companies were not able to afford the large, expensive machines required. Neither could the small businessman afford to hire engineers, managers, or supervisors to run their operations. Research and development personnel, necessary for product improvement and eventual cutting of costs, were also beyond the financial reach of the smaller businessman. In addition, these essential ingredients to successful large-scale industry required large amounts of capital. Therefore, only the larger firms had the necessary funds and backing for the promotion of large-scale industry.

Big business also enjoyed the advantage of mass production. Since production was on such a large scale, these businesses were given discounts for purchasing raw materials in large quantities. Some large organizations could even afford to purchase and maintain their own raw material sources, such as mines or forests.

As industrialism flourished in the United States, so did the corporation system. A corporation was formed when several businessmen combined their capital, equipment, and other assets. Having done this, these businessmen would submit a formal request to the government asking for permission to establish the corporation. Individual investors who bought into the organization received stock in the corporation. These stockholders elected directors who appointed company officials to set and determine corporate policies. When the corporation made profits, the stockholders received a share of these profits. If the corporation failed to make a profit, the stockholders still owned their shares but did not benefit from a profit.

Much of the capital that went into building large corporations came from the shipping and trade businesses prior to the Civil War. Profits made during this period flowed back into businesses to purchase better machines, equipment, and manpower. Industrialists also borrowed money from foreign countries when necessary.

Corporations merged in various ways and for different reasons. The most common type of merger occurred when competing plants that produced the same products found it was in their best interests to combine their assets and form one large business. Other companies found it expedient to merge with closely related industries. These mergers supplied all of their production needs and brought sources of raw materials, manufacturing, and distribution under one management. For example, this merging often occurred in the steel industries that expanded to include coal fields, blast furnaces, and transportation facilities in one organization.

Corporations symbolized big business and became powerful institutions largely through their use of modernized machinery and adoption of streamlined production methods. Organization and management of men and materials, however, was vital to achieving the status of a leading industry. These constantly expanding corporations sought to reduce competition and to gain control by building up **monopolies** in

their trade. By eliminating competition, profits would increase in several ways. Lack of competition not only gave them a larger market but also enabled them to sell goods at higher prices. The elimination of competitors and the increase of profits became the large corporation's major goals. Public benefits, such as reduced consumer costs and the production of quality products, therefore, were not a concern to monopolies.

Consequently, corporations became continually aware of opportunities to gain monopolies in their trade. When depressions caused weaker competitors to declare bankruptcy, large businesses stepped in to buy these floundering firms. Although this **consolidation** trend was barely evident in the 1800s, it became increasingly apparent by the early 1900s. By 1905, 11 percent of the business firms controlled more than 80 percent of the capital, employed 72 percent of the laborers, and produced 79 percent of the manufactured goods, a shocking monopoly of business.

Even though a large amount of corporation profits were generally put back into the business, many individuals became extremely wealthy and influential by pursuing industrial careers. For instance, Edward H. Harriman, William Vanderbilt, and James J. Hill became industrial tycoons in the railroad industry. John D. Rockefeller gained an enormous fortune by controlling most of the oil industry, and Andrew Carnegie made his millions by dominating the steel industry. J.P. Morgan, noted for his banking achievements, accumulated a huge fortune. Henry Ford created a financial empire through the mass production of automobiles.

Among the average working class and smaller businessmen, a deep feeling of fear and resentment arose against the growing economic power of those industrial tycoons and their mighty corporations. However, such opposition proved ineffective against those large industries as did the laws that attempted to control them.

New Product | Invests in Product

Permission forms | Investors receive stock

Stockholders elect Company Officials

Directors

Stock Holders | President

Stockholders profit off corporate stock

| The birth of a corporation

This began to change, however, when Theodore Roosevelt began his term of office. Roosevelt began to strictly enforce the earlier antitrust laws against corporations that he suspected were charging exorbitant prices or selling inferior goods to undercut competition. Although President Roosevelt lost some battles against big business, he succeeded in turning the public against guilty organizations. Thus, Roosevelt was able to gain more cooperation from the larger corporations and obtain fairer treatment of the consumer.

President Wilson was also concerned with the practices of some large corporations. Therefore, Wilson supported the Clayton Antitrust Act of 1914. Although strengthening previous corporation control laws, the *Clayton Antitrust Act* also made illegal certain methods used by big business to crush competition. Another legislative action taken to control big business was the creation of the Federal Trade Commission. The *Commission* was composed of five men appointed by the president and was authorized not only to enforce antitrust laws but also to protect small businesses, thereby giving them a chance to survive against the powerful corporations.

As a result, the negative effects of big business were brought under control by the early 1900s. Antitrust laws controlled such undesirable practices as the elimination of competition and the selling of inferior products. Labor laws were enforced to prevent powerful firms from controlling employee working and living conditions. With these negative trends in industry checked, corporations were largely accepted by the people of the United States in a positive way. People in the United States really wanted economic improvement. Corporations not only employed more workers, decreasing unemployment; but their large-scale production methods also brought lower prices, more variety, and a better quality of merchandise to the consumer.

Accordingly, the United States reaped impressive benefits from the economic advantages of big business as its economy rose to new heights. These benefits were enjoyed not only by American citizens but also by people throughout the world.

Match these items.

2.49 _____ Federal Trade Commission

2.50 _____ Clayton Antitrust Act

2.51 _____ Roosevelt

2.52 _____ business specialists

2.53 _____ consolidation

2.54 _____ stockholders

2.55 _____ monopoly

a. president enforcing early antitrust laws

b. experts in business management

c. merging of several businesses into one

d. fought illegal competition methods

e. committee appointed by the president for corporation control

f. exclusive control of a product

g. corporation tycoons

h. investors in corporations

Write the letter of the correct answer on each line.

2.56 Advantages that corporations brought to the United States included (1) decreased unemployment, (2) lower prices, (3) reduced competition, (4) quality goods, (5) a larger variety of merchandise, (6) increased production. _____

    a. 1, 2, 3, 4, 5   b. 1, 3, 4, 5, 6   c. 1, 2, 4, 5, 6

    d. 1, 2, 3, 4, 5, 6   e. neither 1, 2, 3, 4, 5, nor 6

2.57 Harmful practices used by some corporations included (1) monopoly, (2) prevention of legal competition, (3) control over worker's living and working conditions, (4) antitrust laws, (5) immense consolidations. _____

    a. 1, 2, 3, 4   b. 2, 3, 4, 5   c. 1, 2, 4, 5   d. 1, 2, 3, 5

2.58 Advantages that large corporations had over small business included (1) reduction of unit costs, (2) use of specialists, (3) better organization of men and materials, (4) raw material discounts, (5) mergers to supply all production needs, (6) governmental control. _____

    a. 1, 2, 3, 4, 5   b. 2, 3, 4, 5, 6   c. 1, 2, 4, 5, 6   d. 1, 2, 3, 4, 6

Answer the following question.

2.59 How should the Christian corporation owner's practices have differed from ordinary business practices in the early 1900s? _____

_____

_____

_____

_____

Complete the following activity.

2.60 Write a two-to three-page biography of one of the people mentioned in this section. An inventor or one of the corporation tycoons would be especially interesting. Use any source you find available for your biography.

TEACHER CHECK _____ _____
                                   initials   date

Review the material in this section in preparation for the Self Test. This Self Test will check your mastery of this particular section as well as your knowledge of the previous section.

SELF TEST 2

Answer true or false (each answer, 1 point).

2.01 _____ The system of standardized parts made possible the replacing of broken or worn parts instead of the whole product.

2.02 _____ The Crusades revived European interest in trade and travel.

2.03 _____ Stockholders chose directors and enforced company policies.

2.04 _____ Factories were first powered by water and later by steam.

2.05 _____ By the early 1900s in the United States, the New England and Middle Atlantic states led in manufacturing.

2.06 _____ The Embargo Act of 1807 hindered manufacturing in the United States.

2.07 _____ The War of 1812 increased production in the United States.

2.08 _____ Ford's assembly-line production greatly reduced cost per unit.

2.09 _____ Major goals of corporations were to eliminate competition and to increase profits.

2.010 _____ Monasteries established a pattern for industry in discipline and in specific work responsibilities.

Match these Items (each answer, 2 points).

2.011	_____ Field	a.	iron plow
2.012	_____ Bell	b.	_Clermont_
2.013	_____ Fulton	c.	assembly-line production
2.014	_____ Howe	d.	airplane
2.015	_____ Whitney	e.	transatlantic cable
2.016	_____ Cooper	f.	sewing machine
2.017	_____ Ford	g.	telephone
2.018	_____ McAdam	h.	improved road construction
2.019	_____ Watt	i.	standardized parts
2.020	_____ McCormick	j.	reaping machine
2.021	_____ Wright	k.	steam engine
2.022	_____ Drake	l.	_Tom Thumb_
2.023	_____ Edison	m.	oil well
		n.	light bulb
		o.	wood plow

Complete the following sentences (each answer, 3 points).

2.024   The world-wide change from manual labor to machines was called the _____

_____ .

2.025   The merging of several businesses into one is called _____.

2.026   The _Tom Thumb_ and the _Clermont_ were examples of the use of _____

power in transportation.

2.027   The European nation taking the lead in industry was _____.

2.028   A necessity for beginning industry is the investment of _____.

2.029   The main investors in the early industry of the United States were _____

_____ .

2.030   The first canal in the United States was the _____.

2.031   The United States' first national road was called the _____.

2.032   At the time of the Civil War, the Northern economy was a. _____,

but the Southern economy was largely b. _____.

2.033 The exclusive control of a product by a business is called a _____ of that product.

Write the letter for the correct answer on each line (each answer, 3 points).

2.034 Early European factors that led to the birth of industry were (1) the Crusades, (2) monasteries, (3) early capitalism, (4) feudalism. _____
a. 1, 2, 3   b. 2, 3, 4   c. 1, 2, 4   d. 1, 3, 4

2.035 Requirements for a nation to become industrialized included (1) rich, natural resources, (2) monopolies, (3) many workers, (4) sufficient investment capital. _____
a. 1, 2, 3   b. 2, 3, 4   c. 1, 3, 4   d. 1, 2, 4

2.036 Early American industry was given a boost by (1) the Embargo Act, (2) new production methods, (3) corporations stifling competition, (4) war, (5) transportation and communication improvements, (6) new power sources. _____
a. 1, 2, 3, 4, 5   b. 1, 2, 3, 5, 6   c. 2, 3, 4, 5, 6   d. 1, 2, 4, 5, 6

2.037 Measures controlling the practices of corporations included (1) the Federal Trade Commission, (2) the antitrust laws, (3) consolidation, (4) the Clayton Antitrust Act, (5) labor laws. _____
a. 1, 2, 3, 4   b. 2, 3, 4, 5   c. 1, 2, 4, 5   d. 1, 3, 4, 5

2.038 Corporations found success in using (1) modernized machinery, (2) fewer workers, (3) superior production methods, (4) disciplined organization and management. _____
a. 1, 2, 3   b. 1, 3, 4   c. 2, 3, 4   d. 1, 2, 4

Answer the following questions (each answer, 4 points).

2.039 What factors and attitudes made the United States ripe for industrial growth?

_____

_____

_____

2.040 What sources of power were available to industry by the early 1900s?

_____

_____

_____

2.041 What advantages did corporations bring to the economy of the United States?

_____

_____

_____

2.042 What part did stockholders play in corporations?

_____

_____

<table>
<tr><td>80
100</td><td>SCORE_____</td><td>TEACHER_____ _____
initials   date</td></tr>
</table>

3. SOCIAL CHANGES OF THE INDUSTRIAL REVOLUTION

The advancements in technology and in mass-production methods greatly expanded the potential of this country's industry. The resulting progress did not come without its price, however. The burden of change was intensely felt by the common laborer whose lifestyle and social position were completely revolutionized by the industrialization of United States.

Section Objectives

Review these objectives. When you have completed this section, you should be able to:

7. Explain the social changes resulting from the Industrial Revolution.

    7.1 Describe the urbanized lifestyle as opposed to rural living.

    7.2 Explain the frustrations of living and working conditions on the laborer.

8. Describe the influence of the Industrial Revolution on the world's economy.

Vocabulary

Study these words to enhance your learning success in this section.

bourgeoisie	laissez-faire	collective bargaining
socialism	compensation	tariff

NEGATIVE DRAWBACKS

The Industrial Revolution brought masses of people from outlying farm districts into urban areas in pursuit of a better economic life for themselves and for their families. Although some were successful in achieving these goals, most rural farmers realized too late how difficult the social and economic conditions were in the cities. After selling the little they owned in hopes of bettering their positions, rural families had little choice but to remain in the new situation they had chosen for themselves.

Urbanized lifestyles. The great influx of workers to the city created immense social problems. The most pressing problem was the lack of adequate housing. Many of the workers were unable to afford houses or decent apartments on their meager wages. Therefore, two or more families often shared one floor of an apartment dwelling. This situation was the forerunner of tenement housing in today's large cities. The tenement houses were three to six stories high with each floor divided into separate family units. These houses were often overcrowded, poorly ventilated, and dimly lit with some rooms having no windows at all. The houses were bad enough in good weather; however, conditions became desperate during hot, humid summers or damp, freezing winters when heating systems were sadly inadequate. Tenement dwellers also suffered from the lack of proper garbage disposal and poor sanitation, thereby increasing the risk of disease. Also, water posed an additional hardship, with several families relying on a single source. Furthermore, the crowded, disorganized, and poorly kept tenements were dangerous fire traps.

Prior to automobiles and trains, inefficient transportation also created difficulties for the city worker. Most people had to walk through crowded streets to their respective jobs. Mass transportation systems were slow in developing and were seldom adequate. The overcrowded, frustrating urban conditions encouraged crime, especially in slum areas. Immorality was more the rule than the exception. To combat this immorality, church organizations and gospel missions conducted their outreach ministries for Jesus Christ, shining the only ray of light onto many hopeless souls. In Christ, man can be confident (Philippians 4:19) that his needs will be provided and can be content (Philippians 4:11) in whatever state he finds himself.

One of the most successful outreaches in the cities was (and is) the Salvation Army®. Founded in England in 1878 by William Booth, the Army reached out to the inner city poor with the message of salvation and basic necessities like food, clothes, and shelter. The founders of the Salvation Army® in America arrived in 1880. Organized like an army using military names and terms, the Salvation Army® enjoyed widespread results. Even today it is one of the largest suppliers of food and shelter for the poor in America.

The farm worker had enjoyed a life of relative independence and wholesomeness. Setting his own hours, the farmer worked hard; but farming was a satisfying labor. The farmer was his own boss and in control of his own life. The drastically opposing lifestyle of factory working and city living was a shocking contrast. The confinements of city life and factory labor entrenched him in economic slavery. With his independence gone, the factory worker had to rely on others for employment, housing, and food. The freedom he enjoyed in his former country atmosphere was exchanged for the fears and anxieties of city dwelling.

| Tenement living

In the early days of the Industrial Revolution, workers had very little to show for the wealth or comforts they helped to manufacture. Out of these conditions arose the theories of communism. Karl Marx, a German, carefully observed this exploitation of the proletariat by the wealthy industrialists whom he called capitalists. In the unsuccessful German revolution of 1848, Marx and Friedrich Engels wrote the *Communist Manifesto*, which outlined the theory that working-class revolutionaries should overthrow their capitalistic masters. Later fleeing to England where they lived in freedom, Marx and Engels wrote *Das Kapital*, which is the theoretical basis of communism and **socialism**.

The struggle between the capitalist **bourgeoisie** and the working proletariat was brought to a head by the Industrial Revolution. Marx's contention was that labor really produced all wealth, but only received a small portion of the value it produced. Marx argued that capitalist owners were the recipients of the wealth in the form of profits. Marx further stressed that this imbalance could be changed as the time grew ripe for the proletariat to rise up and overthrow the bourgeoisie rulers.

The Marxist movement, which claimed that social ownership and operation of production could be achieved gradually, peaceably, and even democratically, was called socialism. On the other hand, the group of Marxist socialists who preached that the class struggle would end in war called themselves communists.

Communism proclaimed that after seizing power through force and violence, the proletariat would then rule until a utopian state of socialistic government could be established. In reality, when communist states were created, the leaders ruled as dictators, giving the people no voice at all. Life for the workers became even harsher as they lost all freedom to make their own decisions and often faced economic hardship when their leaders tried to outproduce the capitalist countries using force and rigid planning.

At some point in time, communist governments existed in Russia, China, North Korea, Vietnam, Cuba, most of the nations of Eastern Europe, and several African nations. By the early 1990s these had largely failed and returned to a form of democracy. Even those that remained officially communist often no longer followed traditional communist economic policies; but, they did maintain dictatorial control over their people. So, in the modern era we have the paradox of Communist China with a capitalist economy enjoying a huge economic boom in the 1980s and 1990s.

 Write the letter of the correct answer on each line.

3.1 Factors luring rural families to the city included (1) higher wages, (2) better lifestyle, (3) wholesome environment, (4) variety of entertainment. _____

a. 1, 2, 3   b. 2, 3, 4   c. 1, 2, 4   d. 1, 3, 4

3.2 Problems facing tenement dwellers included (1) cramped quarters, (2) poor sanitary conditions, (3) crime and immorality, (4) poor housing, (5) efficient lighting. _____

a. 1, 2, 3, 4   b. 2, 3, 4, 5   c. 1, 3, 4, 5   d. 1, 2, 3, 5

3.3 Factors giving rise to the theories of Marx included (1) abuses dealt to the working class, (2) understanding bosses, (3) poor conditions under which laborers lived and worked, (4) employers taking advantage of employees, (5) lack of profits given employees. _____

a. 1, 2, 3, 4   b. 2, 3, 4, 5   c. 1, 2, 3, 5   d. 1, 3, 4, 5

3.4 Communists (1) support a type of socialism, (2) believe that the working class could overcome through force, (3) agree with the free enterprise system, (4) seek to set up a future ideal socialist government. _____

a. 1, 2, 3   b. 2, 3, 4   c. 1, 2, 4   d. 1, 3, 4

Answer the following questions.

3.5 As a farmer turned factory worker, compare your lifestyle in the city with that of the country. Which do you prefer, and why?

_____

_____

_____

_____

_____

_____

_____

3.6 Research the advantages communists claimed they had over the free enterprise system. Prepare an argument defending either communism or the free enterprise system in the United States. State your arguments clearly.

_____

_____

_____

_____

_____

_____

_____

_____

TEACHER CHECK _____ _____
                              initials   date

Factory frustrations. Factory working conditions and urban living conditions were similar in the early years of industry, and both were despicably inhumane. Working hours were long and hard, often from sunrise to sunset. Fourteen to sixteen hours a day was generally considered a normal work load for men, women, and even children. Poorly ventilated factories were hot and steamy during the summer months and cold and drafty during the winter. Also, safety and sanitary conditions were poor, and serious and sometimes fatal injuries were quite common. Accident insurance or injury compensation was nonexistent. Wages, already at meager levels for men, were even lower for women and children.

One of the most abominable aspects of the early years of the Industrial Revolution was its treatment of women and children. Children who had not even reached their sixth birthday were mercilessly put to work in mills and mines. In coal mines women were used to pull the carts of coal, and children pushed the heavy loads in areas too low for horses or mules. In factories women were often forced to work on their hands and knees under the harsh discipline of threatening supervisors. Children worked until exhausted and were cruelly beaten if found sleeping at their assigned tasks.

Consequently, work in factories was often uncertain and unsteady. Sometimes goods were manufactured so rapidly and in such great quantities that those goods would often accumulate at the factory, waiting to be purchased or shipped. When this accumulation occurred, employers would cut already meager wages and reduce production. The dreaded layoff often lasted until business increased. This increase in business sometimes took months or sometimes ended in the closing of the company. Unemployment was feared by all workers, and no unemployment insurance was available to meet needs during times of such crises. In addition, the workers had no retirement pensions; consequently, unless the unemployed worker received charity, he was literally faced with starvation.

Although the plight of the workers was known to the government, their grievances were not acted upon. This lack of action was caused mainly by a laissez-faire policy in economics and politics. Many leaders in the economic and political communities held firmly to the ideas of economist Adam Smith. Smith explained that business activities were based on two natural economic laws: (1) the law of supply and demand, and (2) the law of competition. According to these laws, if the supply of a product is down and the demand for it is great, the product will get a higher price because of its scarcity. As a result, both prices and profits will go up, allowing capitalists to invest more money in factories to produce the product in demand. When the supply of this product increases, competition between manufacturers will increase. Smith's theory totally forbade interference by government in the operation of these private businesses; therefore, governments remained silent, approving of the economic benefits the industries were providing.

The philosophy of laissez-faire began to lose popularity, however, as workers' cries for improvement continually were refused or ignored by most businesses. The terrible abuse suffered by English workers finally forced moral legislators to institute reforms. This breakthrough for the factory laborer resulted largely from the arousal of public sentiment against the deplorable working conditions revealed in the writings of authors Charles Dickens and Benjamin Disraeli. On the other hand, wealthy landowners and nobles resented the rising standard of living of the middle class and searched for laws to hamper their progress. During the early part of the nineteenth century, a series of much needed labor reform laws began in England. In 1819 children under nine years of age were prohibited from working in cotton mills, and children between the ages of nine and eighteen were not allowed to work

| An old mining cart

over twelve hours per day. Expanded in 1833 to cover all textile factories, this law also prohibited night work for all children under eighteen years of age. In 1847 the Ten-Hour Act was passed, stating that women and children could only work ten hours a day. Because factories were so dependent upon women and children, the ten hour workday became a general practice for all textile workers.

Moreover, laws were also passed improving safety and sanitary conditions that were regularly enforced by inspections. Other countries soon followed England's example in dealing with the plight of their factory workers. The laissez-faire theories about industry were gradually replaced by a government more sensitive to the needs of its working class.

As long as harsh labor conditions existed, workers rallied to take the initiative to protect themselves. Although disagreements and lack of unity caused temporary setbacks, labor ultimately became organized. Consequently, by offering a strong and united front, the working man would have some leverage in dealing with big business.

Unions also organized to take a stand against employer's abuses. On an individual basis, such an attempt would have failed since an average worker had little opportunity to bargain with his employer. The little contact the worker had with factory managers and supervisors was inconsequential. The factory managers and the supervisors were employees lacking the authority to change wages or working conditions.

Unfortunately, factory reform laws did not bring about a change in wages; but they did improve working conditions. Workers needed a leader to confront their employers with their demands for higher wages. By forming unions, labor leaders were able to bargain for the improved conditions of all laborers. Factory workers now were able to force industrialists to listen to their grievances through a process called **collective bargaining**. If industrialists did not hear the workers out, the entire work force would cease labor and strike until a mutual settlement could be reached. Although they were not paid while on strike, the outcome would benefit workers in the long run.

Factory owners dreaded the prospect of strikes because of lost production while they still had business costs to meet.

Although collective bargaining negotiations were often difficult, the end result for the work force was well worth the effort. As equalizers in the balance of industry's power, unions gave the common laborer a voice in the negotiations. With years of needless suffering behind them, the agony of the past gave way to hope for a brighter future.

Answer true or false.

3.7 _____ Early factory workers labored twelve hours a day.

3.8 _____ Unemployment was feared by early laborers.

3.9 _____ Adam Smith endorsed a laissez-faire policy in economics.

3.10 _____ Dickens wrote about deplorable factory conditions in England.

3.11 _____ Unions did much to increase factory pay.

3.12 _____ Strikes were called if employers did not improve conditions.

3.13 _____ Employers lost money during strikes even though workers were not paid during strikes.

Answer the following question.

3.14 What does the Bible have to say concerning employee-employer relationships and how each should treat the other? Work with a friend and record your answers here.

_____

_____

_____

_____

_____

TEACHER CHECK _____ _____

initials   date

POSITIVE CONTRIBUTIONS

Whatever the claims of socialists and communists, the accomplishments of the free enterprise system have been amazing, in spite of the unfortunate past. The increased production and quick distribution of goods allowed the industrialized nations to exceed anything the world has ever experienced in terms of security, recreation, relaxation, and health. With much of the cruel and exhausting work forbidden by law in factories and agriculture, many of the negative aspects of industry have been greatly reduced.

Increase in economy. Under the free enterprise system, the Industrial Revolution raised the world's standard of living. The services and goods produced continued to bring prosperity, making even poor countries seem wealthy compared to their economic status a century ago. Although many economic problems still remain to be solved, most of the problems will ultimately be worked out by the same determined effort that has solved the problem of production.

Most of the successes of the Industrial Revolution did not occur through radical terrorists who advocated the overthrow of the capitalistic system. Success came through reforms made within the system itself. The answer to improvement does not lie in a revolution of force or violence, but rather in a patient and consistent stand through means of debating, compromising, and bargaining.

Industrial improvements came mainly as a result of laws passed by the democratic process or through the organization of labor unions using the collective bargaining technique. These improvements did not always come without resistance from both labor and management. However, firm negotiations are a far cry from the *overthrow-of-capitalism* policies of both the socialist and communist camps.

The expansion of industry would have never occurred without the tremendous increase in the market for manufactured goods. The great demand for products resulted in an abundant supply. This expansion was due largely to an ever increasingly well paid population that continually demanded the products of industry. The growth of better communications and cheaper transportation that provided for a wider distribution of goods also contributed to the industry's boom.

Because of the rise in the economic level of both the producer and the consumer, mass production was required to satisfy the appetite of the world's markets. Highly industrialized nations sometimes produce more than they can consume; therefore, international trade and commerce developed. No modern-day nation is absolutely self-sufficient. To prosper, a nation needs this mutual exchange of raw materials and products with other nations. Consequently, the industrial countries of the world rely quite heavily on international trade. Also, industrialized nations sell surplus goods abroad so that they might purchase the products and materials they need from other countries to maintain a balance of trade.

When foreign dealers price their products lower than those on the home market, however, international trade can cause severe domestic problems. To protect themselves from such an occurrence, businessmen in industrialized countries operated within the framework of those governments that offered protection from competitive foreign businesses which attempted to undersell their products. For protection, tariffs, or taxes, were placed on less expensive imports. This levy raised import prices, thereby protecting internal business and establishing a stable economy within the country.

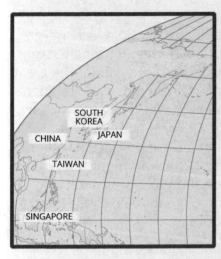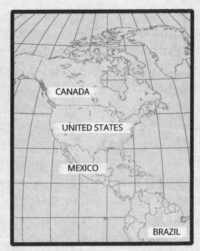

Ten Leading Countries in U.S. Foreign Trade (2010)
(total trade in billions)

Canada	$525,300	United Kingdom	$98,300
China	$456,800	Korea, South	$87,700
Mexico	$393,000	France	$65,600
Japan	$180,900	Taiwan	$61,900
Federal Republic of Germany	$130,900	Brazil	$59,300

U.S. Census Bureau

There is a danger in this practice, however. If tariffs become too high, problems will also result. For example, a high tariff can drop a country's sales so low they cannot afford to import necessary products from other countries. When sales decrease too much, products may accumulate and gradually stop. Trade stagnates, layoffs increase, and a recession or a depression may occur. In an industrialized world where nations are dependent upon each other for the consumption of goods, depression could spread and place the economy of the entire world in jeopardy. The continual prosperity of the world's economy is filled with complexities and is dependent upon international cooperation in order to function at its best.

The Industrial Revolution forever changed the simple, self-sufficient nations of the world. Increased production brought increased demands for large-scale and wide-spread distribution. Not only were the economies of England and the United States elevated, but as nation traded with nation, the interdependency for raw materials and products reached to every part of the world.

Complete the following sentences.

3.15 The Industrial Revolution raised the world's _____ .

3.16 An abundant supply of products becomes available when there is an increase in the

_____ .

3.17 Wider distribution of goods was made possible by a. _____

and b. _____ .

3.18 Nations a. _____ surplus goods in order to b. _____

needed products and materials.

3.19 Taxes placed on imported goods to raise their prices are called _____ .

3.20 The continual prosperity of our world's economy is dependent upon _____

_____ .

Answer the following questions.

3.21 How did democratic nations successfully improve and reform industry?

_____

_____

3.22 How has the Industrial Revolution influenced and changed the world's economy?

_____

_____

3.23 How would you explain the interdependence of present-day nations on each other for trade
and commerce?

_____

_____

_____

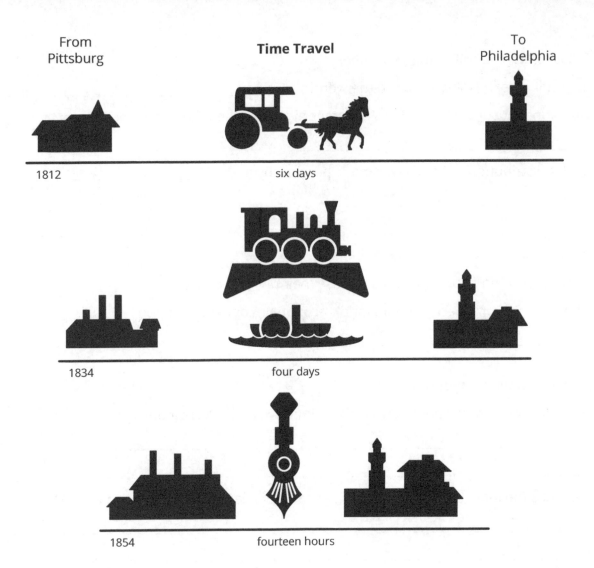

From Pittsburg	Time Travel	To Philadelphia
1812	six days	
1834	four days	
1854	fourteen hours	

Availability of products. The Industrial Revolution's phenomenal impact was felt throughout the world's trade markets. Mass consumption demanded mass production and kept factories operating and economies flourishing. To fully appreciate how modern age methods of transportation boosted the distribution of mass produced goods to widespread world markets, consider transportation as it was in the Middle Ages.

During the Dark Ages in Europe, roads were few and inadequate. Furthermore, bridges were scarce and unreliable. Travelers were fearful of bandits and pirates who roamed the land and sea. Feudal lords charged high taxes for the use of any roads, bridges, and water routes that touched their domain. Even certain laws of the Roman Catholic Church made travel difficult, and trade was nearly stifled by such travel conditions. The trade that did exist occurred at fairs organized by feudal lords for purely selfish reasons, their own personal prosperity. The growth of the Industrial Revolution, however, drastically changed this concept of trade, commerce, and transportation.

As the Western world grew out of the Middle Ages and its thinking, the change in transportation modes played a valuable part in revolutionizing the economic world. Providing greatly reduced travel expenses for passengers and manufactured goods, better transportation also encouraged the shipment of raw materials, increased business markets, and strongly stimulated industrial growth in general.

Land travel was greatly enhanced by the road designers of the Industrial Revolution. McAdam's use of crushed rock in road construction, which was mentioned earlier, was a tremendous improvement in making road travel safer and more comfortable. The railroad and the steam locomotive quickened both the delivery of goods and travel; however, as a mode of travel the railroad had its anxious moments. Riding a railroad train in its early years was quite an adventurous undertaking. Modeled after stagecoaches, the first railroad cars were tied together with chains, making the ride bumpy, jerky, and quite uncomfortable. Because of the necessity of track switching, passengers had to make a seemingly endless number of changes from one train to another. Train fires and derailments added to the many hazards of rail travel.

| Steam train

Water travel also underwent great changes during the industrial age. The canal systems of England, Europe, and the United States eliminated the many delays along land routes and did much to improve national trade and commerce. The pattern set by Fulton's steamboat began a new age in water traffic. To conduct world trade, large cargo ships sailed the oceans powered by new steam engines. Eliminating endless delays caused by lack of wind, tons of cargo were shipped by the steamboat.

The seemingly simple change from manual labor to machine production caused a complex economic upheaval, affecting not only economies and lifestyles, but man himself. The changes of the Industrial Revolution have not ended. New inventions are being created daily, tested, and put into use that constantly change the technological world in which we live.

✎ **Answer the following questions.**

3.24 What impact did the new methods of transportation have on the availability of products?
Explain. _____

_____

_____

3.25 Why was trade so poor during the Middle Ages? _____

_____

_____

3.26 What influence did the following transportation improvements have on distribution and travel?

a. crushed rock roads _____

b. canals _____

c. steamboats _____

d. steam locomotives _____

↺ **Before taking this last Self Test, you may want to do one or more of these self checks.**

1. _____ Read the objectives. Determine if you can do them.

2. _____ Restudy the material related to any objectives that you cannot do.

3. _____ Use the **SQ3R** study procedure to review the material.

    a. **S**can the sections.

    b. **Q**uestion yourself again (review the questions you wrote initially).

    c. **R**ead to answer your questions.

    d. **R**ecite the answers to yourself.

    e. **R**eview areas you didn't understand.

4. _____ Review all vocabulary, activities, and Self Tests, writing a correct answer for each
wrong answer.

SELF TEST 3

Match these Items (each answer, 2 points).

3.01 _____ urbanization

3.02 _____ socialism

3.03 _____ laissez-faire

3.04 _____ free enterprise

3.05 _____ capitalism

3.06 _____ collective bargaining

3.07 _____ Industrial Revolution

3.08 _____ assembly line

3.09 _____ standardized parts

3.010 _____ consolidation

3.011 _____ monopoly

3.012 _____ stockholders

3.013 _____ Federal Trade Commission

a. the piece-by-piece assembling of a product

b. negotiations between labor and management

c. mass movement to the city

d. private ownership and distribution of goods competitively in a free market

e. opposed government intervention in private business

f. collective or government ownership of production and distribution

g. change from manual labor to machine

h. poor working conditions for employees

i. merger of several businesses into one

j. interchangeable parts

k. freedom of private business to compete and operate for a profit

l. exclusive control of a product

m. controlled corporation practices

n. investors in corporations who share in the profits

Answer true or false (each answer, 1 point).

3.014 _____ The working methods of Whitney and Ford made mass production possible.

3.015 _____ Industrialized methods were first used in England's iron industry.

3.016 _____ Plentiful natural resources and work force are musts for industry.

3.017 _____ Wars and corporations hindered the growth of industry in the United States.

3.018 _____ New England businessmen were heavy investors in industry.

3.019 _____ The Crusades revived European interest in trade and business.

3.020 _____ The *Communist Manifesto* is considered an important work on socialism.

3.021 _____ Smith wrote of the deplorable factory conditions in England.

3.022 _____ By the early 1900s the North Central and Middle Atlantic states led in production in the United States.

3.023 _____ Nations import their surplus goods in order to export needed items.

3.024 _____ Lumber and textiles were the top ranking U.S. industries by the 1900s.

3.025 _____ The Crusades and monasteries were early European influences on industry.

3.026 _____ Major goals of corporations were to eliminate competition and increase profits.

Complete the following sentences (each answer, 3 points).

3.027 Watt, Fulton, and Stephenson all experimented with the _____ .

3.028 Field, Bell, and Morse developed great improvements in _____ .

3.029 The deciding factor of the North's victory in the Civil War was its _____ .

3.030 Marx's theories of socialism were outlined in the _____ .

3.031 Communists believe in the seizure of _____ power by force.

3.032 Labor unions gave a voice against employer abuse to _____ .

3.033 Laissez-faire economy was based on the law of a. _____

and the law of b. _____ .

3.034 McCormick, Whitney, and Oliver contributed to the United States' _____

_____ .

3.035 Tariffs balance the economy by raising the prices of _____ .

3.036 High taxes and robbers threatened trade during the _____ .

3.037 Technological improvement in transportation and _____

aided the fighting of wars.

Write the letter for the correct answer on each line (each answer, 2 points).

3.038 American industry was aided by (1) war, (2) new power sources, (3) improvements in transportation and communication, (4) new production methods, (5) monopolies. _____
   a. 1, 2, 3, 4   b. 2, 3, 4, 5   c. 1, 2, 4, 5   d. 1, 2, 3, 5

3.039 Factors making the United States ripe for industry's growth included (1) abundant natural resources, (2) ample work force, (3) help from England, (4) investment capital, (5) determination to prove itself. _____
   a. 1, 2, 3, 4   b. 2, 3, 4, 5   c. 1, 2, 4, 5   d. 1, 2, 3, 5

3.040 Factors aiding the plight of factory workers included (1) labor improvement laws, (2) laissez-faire, (3) labor unions, (4) books by Dickens and Disraeli. _____
   a. 1, 2, 3, 4   b. 1, 3, 4   c. 2, 3, 4   d. 1, 2, 4

3.041 Advantages corporations brought to the United States included (1) lowered unemployment, (2) reduced competition, (3) lower prices, (4) better quality goods, (5) larger variety of merchandise. _____
   a. 1, 2, 3, 4   b. 2, 3, 4, 5   c. 1, 3, 4, 5   d. 1, 2, 3, 5

3.042 Social changes resulting from the Industrial Revolution included (1) urbanization, (2) greater independence, (3) growing socialism, (4) poor living and working conditions. _____
   a. 1, 3, 4   b. 2, 3, 4   c. 1, 2, 3   d. 1, 2, 4

Answer the following questions (each answer, 4 points).

3.043 What were the factors that gave rise to communism? _____

_____

3.044 What measures were created and used by Roosevelt and later presidents to control

corporation practices? _____

_____

_____

3.045 How has the Industrial Revolution affected the world's economy? _____

_____

_____

3.046 How did the Industrial Revolutions in Europe and England affect the growth of industry in

the United States? _____

_____

_____

80/100   **SCORE** _____   **TEACHER** _____ _____
                                                                       initials   date

Before taking the LIFEPAC Test, you may want to do one or more of these self checks.

1. _____ Read the objectives. Check to see if you can do them.
2. _____ Restudy the material related to any objectives that you cannot do.
3. _____ Use the SQ3R study procedure to review the material.
4. _____ Review activities, Self Tests, and LIFEPAC vocabulary words.
5. _____ Restudy areas of weakness indicated by the last Self Test.

GLOSSARY

aristocracy .... The small, privileged class of nobility or the very wealthy.

bourgeoisie .... The middle class, especially those having views influenced by private-property interest.

capital .... The amount of property or money available for use in business.

capitalism .... The economic system characterized by private ownership and the distribution of goods competitively in a free market.

capitalist .... A person who has capital invested in business, and one who engages in free enterprise.

collective bargaining .... Negotiations between an employer and union representatives concerning wages, hours, and working conditions.

compensation .... Payment to an unemployed or injured worker or his family.

consolidation .... The merging of businesses into one large organization.

free enterprise .... The freedom of private business to operate competitively for profit and without undue government intervention.

industrialism .... Social organization in which industries, especially large scale ones, are dominant.

laissez-faire .... The policy opposing government intervention in economics.

mobilized .... Assembled and ready for war duty.

monopoly .... The exclusive control by a business of a commodity or production.

proletariat .... The laboring class, especially those who lack their own means of production, thus selling their labor in order to live.

sequestered .... Withdrawn or secluded.

socialism .... Any of a number of economic and political theories advocating collective or governmental ownership of the means of production and distribution of goods.

standardized .... Brought to conformity; making all alike.

tariff .... Taxes on imported goods.